Caring for Kathleen

A Sister's Story about Down's Syndrome and Dementia

Margaret T. Fray

British Library Cataloguing in Publication Data

A CIP record for this book is available from the British Library

ISBN 1 902519 19 1

© Copyright 2000 BILD Publications

BILD Publications is the publishing office of the
British Institute of Learning Disabilities
Wolverhampton Road
Kidderminster
Worcestershire
United Kingdom
DY10 3PP

Telephone: 01562 850251
Fax: 01562 851970
e-mail: bild@bild.demon.co.uk

BILD Publications are distributed worldwide by
Plymbridge Distributors Limited
Plymbridge House
Estover Road
Plymouth
United Kingdom
PL6 7PZ

Telephone: 01752 202301
Fax: 01752 202333

Acknowledgements

The author would like to express her special thanks to Linda Averill and her colleagues at BILD for their support. Personal thanks also, to her friend Dinah Robinson, Community Learning Disability Nurse, who encouraged her to write this story, and to Percy Moore, for his patience and understanding.

The production of this publication was supported by a grant from the Department of Health.

Terminology

It is BILD policy to use the term Down syndrome in our publications. However, as this is a personal story, we have used Margaret Fray's preferred terminology - Down's Syndrome.

FOR KATHLEEN ANNE

My gentle little sister.

Together we travelled

To the end of the road

And I have kept my promise.

This is your story.

My Sister Kathleen

My sister, Kathleen, was born about 6 a.m. on Friday, the 15th July, 1927, at the home of her grandparents; the day before, my mother had pushed me on the swing under the big tree on the front lawn; today my grandmother was taking me upstairs to meet my new baby sister for the first time. In the warm summer sunshine, overcome with sudden shyness, I went behind a chair in the window-bay, and bit into a pearl bobble hanging from my mother's dress, over the back of the chair. I still have the bobble with the mark of my teeth - a memento of the first time that I saw Kathleen. She had arrived with the condition known as Down's syndrome, although few used that terminology in those days and, of course, I was not aware of it then - I would be four years old the following week, and the life expectancy then for a child with this syndrome was nine years.[1]

We two were the only children, and I think that, as a family, we made as happy a life for Kathleen as was possible, despite the fact that throughout our lives our father suffered from his experiences during the First World War; his own life was mainly hell; he often made our lives hell too, and those were Kathleen's formative years; but we had a wonderful mother. Looking back, I don't know how she stayed - but attitudes to marriage were different then, and Kathleen had a lovely, brave spirit of her own; a true "Friday's child" - loving and giving - she made one happy, just by being with her.

At the time of her birth, there was no Welfare State; on every occasion that she required medical treatment - and those were frequent in the early days - the doctor's bill had to be met by our parents and the medicine bought from the chemist.

Most children born with Down's syndrome in those times were regarded as ineducable, and there were very few special schools for children with any form of disability. Those who had Down's syndrome in particular, were not expected to outlive their parents, and no provision was made for them in that event. Many parents simply accepted the responsibility of caring for their children without any thought of state assistance, while others let them be placed in institutional care - sometimes for reasons of poverty, and not because the child was unwanted or unloved. Mothers who had to go out to work could not leave these children at home alone, and there must have been many aching hearts, for they are often exceptionally loving children.

Our own mother was advised in 1927 to put her daughter into an institution and try to forget that she had been born; similar advice is still sometimes given in this day and age, as evidenced by Georgie Hill, wife of Damon, the racing driver, in a press report.[2]

When the children live at home, it has usually been the case that the carers make such a good job of the caring that it has not been considered that much help is needed - often to the great detriment of the health of all concerned.

Before the advent of antibiotics and modern heart surgery, the majority of children with Down's syndrome succumbed to chest infections and/or heart malfunctions at an early age. As Kathleen's life-span grew beyond the expected time this gave rise to the often repeated and hurtful exclamation, "Oh! I didn't think they lived that long," as if she came from another planet.

Kathleen's mother was told soon after the birth that her daughter would never sit up, or walk, or talk, but she took her to a Dr Charles Paget Lapage in Liverpool, said to specialise in the condition. He advised that, with great effort from both mother and child, Kathleen might achieve 'some kind of life'. He said that as most of her learning would be by mimicry she should live among ordinary people, and not be confined with others who might be worse than herself. He also suggested bathing in warmed seawater to strengthen the lax muscles, which resulted in my father taking clean petrol cans to the edge of the tide every two days; fortunately we lived by the sea. Then of course, there were the prayers. "More things are wrought by prayer than this world dreams of" was forever being quoted. This was about the sum total of help available in those days.

Attitudes

In our early days, possibly because those children with Down's syndrome were refused formal education, other children may have seen them as alien beings, for sometimes, if there was no adult in sight, we were cruelly tormented and mocked by the rougher element among them. Although I was very young, some instinct prevented me from ever telling our mother - maybe I thought she had enough worries. These incidents gave me early insight into the vulnerability of people with learning disabilities, and later led to a resolve to do what I could to help them to protect their rights. Our happiest playtimes by far were spent with our cousins, who never made any distinction, but they did not live nearby. For Kathleen it was a lonely childhood; although we had each other, I went to school and she had to stay at home. She never showed resentment - that was not in her nature - but she longed to go with me, and I was sad to leave her behind.

Certainly there was prejudice, and discrimination, and those still exist, but the modern media has helped to make the condition much better known and, one hopes, better understood. This awareness has led to some children with Down's syndrome being integrated into mainstream schools and going on to further education, and has induced more people to volunteer their services through various projects which bring greater fulfilment for some, but there is a long way yet to go for many.[3] This is still a pretty hard and cruel world for anyone born different from the so-called norm - whatever that is. The little ones may find more favour than in times past, but it would seem to be a very different story when they try to find interesting occupations or useful employment in their after-school years. Despite the increased awareness and integration, from my experience with my sister, and from what I know of other, younger lives today, it is always going to be an uphill course, although fewer people stare so openly now, as the hills are climbed. We met with a great deal of kindness along the way, but all the kindness in the world could not blot out the pain of those times when that bright, trusting little face turned up to mine and asked, "Why are they staring at me?"

While many people with Down's syndrome may exhibit some similarities in physical features, they enjoy the same variations in life-style as everyone else, each having their own likes and dislikes. To generalise, as some do, for instance by remarking that "they all love music", is very wrong. We have friends of different age groups, one of whom is very shy and retiring, preferring not to socialise, spending a lot of time in his own room with his music and television. Another cannot bear to be alone; he needs to be always in company and likes to be the centre of attention. One child may be out of nappies at the appropriate age - another may still need to use them for many years. From babyhood onwards, the degree of progress varies from person to person, and in this matter I can only speak with any accuracy in regard to my own sister.

Learning to get around

At about eighteen months Kathleen was able to sit up unaided and, although unable to stand alone, began to propel herself across the floor by sitting with her left leg folded at a right angle and with the right leg rowing herself across the room, sometimes at great speed. Then came the day - near her fourth birthday - when she rowed herself across the floor, but at the far end reached out to the handle of a big chest of drawers and pulled herself up to a standing position. Our mother put her hand on my arm and her finger to her lips, to quieten me; we held our breath as Kathleen let go of the handle, turned, and with her arms out-stretched half-ran, half-walked across to us, all smiles. It was a wonderful, never-to-be-forgotten moment; her face was full of joy, and from then on, she always walked. I don't know if it was due to the way she had shuffled across the floor in those early years, but when she did finally walk, her left leg was always slightly bent outwards, and the foot pointed inwards a little. Once she got going, she walked miles with mother and me, for we lived in the country, and she never had any trouble with her leg in walking, so far as we knew. She did, however, always prefer to hold one's hand when outside; any unevenness in the ground would cause her to stumble, and she was always very wary of steps and stairs. In later years, whenever she met a baby, she would worry, asking "Will it walk?" because she always remembered the first time she walked, after wanting to for so long.

From very early days our mother had told me to be careful not to knock Kathleen's head as we played, and had guided my fingers over the soft spot, the fontanelle, where the two sides of the skull grow together at the top, much more slowly in a child with Down's syndrome than is the general rule.

For the next five years or so she would often demonstrate the flexibility of her muscles by doing the 'splits' and, lying on her stomach, bringing her feet over her shoulders. She had seen no-one do that, and no-one had shown her how - she just knew that she could do it, and loved to show off her 'act'. She loved to be the star of the show, even at that early stage!

Kathleen and Peggy with their Mother
in 1928

Kathleen and Peggy in 1931

Kathleen aged 5 with her 'rubber doll'

Growing Up with Down's Syndrome

Learning to speak

From about the age of eighteen months, when she became able to properly grip something with her hands, our mother gave her a wooden-backed hand mirror to hold. She taught her to look first at our mother's mouth, shaping the sounds of the alphabet, one at a time, and then at her own reflection in the mirror, until she began to understand what her mother wanted her to do. I remember how she thought the way she looked saying "O" was very funny. Ever so slowly, and with tremendous patience on mother's part, Kathleen began to make the sounds, and then came the first words, "Dada", "Mama", "Peggy". Her own name was too complicated for her at this stage, so she was called "Baba" for years, but eventually she progressed from "Kaqueleen" to "Kathleen". Later, if we slipped back and called her "Baba" she would laugh and say, "I'm not Baba, I'm a young lady now, I'm Kathleen."

She developed a bad stammer, especially with T's, K's, and S's, but mother would put a finger across Kathleen's lips to tell her to stop, wait, and try again. Sometimes the stammer was so bad her little body shook with it, until she stopped trying. Later she learned to put her own finger across her lips to stop the stammer, and her eyes would smile at being able to do that for herself. Gradually the stammering came less often, and finally disappeared altogether. Through these years and until the late 1940s we lived under great duress, caused by our father's heavy drinking and his neurasthenia gradually worsening, due to the trauma of his war experiences. When I was nine, the doctor kept me at home from school for six months, as I had 'strained nerves', and it was at about that time that Kathleen began to stammer.

For about two years most of the sounds she joined together did not make sense to anyone except me, but by some quirk of nature I always knew exactly what Kathleen was trying to say. Her eyes would watch my mouth as I translated to our parents what she had just said, and she would beam, and nod, and sometimes clap her hands. The strange fact was that she understood what I was saying for her, but she could not yet herself put the sounds in correct juxtaposition. She knew what she was saying, and so did I, but no-one else knew. I can't explain how I knew, I just did, and I can only think that at this stage she taught herself, by watching my lips form the words she had just tried, but failed, to produce. We had a system of hand signals too; she would watch my hands, and use her own to reply to me. There was no explanation for it - it was something just between the two of us, and we both knew exactly what we meant.

Slowly, more and more words came, and this prolonged process grew into a game of putting things to words, so that she learned what objects were called. Mother would ask her to bring, say, a jug, and she might bring two or three items before the right one, and then she enjoyed being told she was a clever girl, and as she gained more words the stammering lessened. The difficulties for her in learning pronunciation were enormous; in common with many others who have this syndrome, her tongue was very much larger both in length and thickness than is usual, making it so much harder for her to produce coherent sound. TH and V were particularly difficult, and she often made D for TH and B for V, although with extra effort she could produce them correctly. She succeeded in learning to speak only with tremendous effort and determination, because she had such an intense desire to be able to speak. The stammering, which mercifully vanished once she could speak, may partly have been caused by her great anxiety to be able to communicate properly.

After she was about eight, and had a full vocabulary, I might remind her of a word from our secret language, and it became a family joke when one day I spoke of the "weege", which was what she had called the sewing-machine, and she replied, "Don't be silly, it's a sewing machine."

Learning to read and write

By now mother had taught her to write block capitals, and I began to find words printed between the lines of some of my precious reading books, for reading was my greatest joy, but I was only too pleased to see her words there. She wanted always to use her left hand; when mother tried to get her to use her right hand, the stammering briefly returned, but by leaving her to use her left hand it disappeared again. Gradually she learned to write sentences, and although she was never able to master joined-up writing, by the time she was twelve she was writing very quickly in extremely small, neat block capitals.

At the same time as learning to write, mother was teaching her to read, and although for many years her progress was slow, suddenly, at the age of seventeen, everything seemed to come together. One of my friends enjoyed the cricket commentaries on the wireless, and Kathleen wanted to be able to say when these would be on air. This was the apparent stimulus, and suddenly she was reading the newspapers, books, stories about the Royal family, film stars, Rupert annuals - everything. But basically this was all due to the everlasting patient teaching of our mother over the previous decade, and I think I helped a little too - as well as Kathleen's own determination to succeed.

Learning and leisure

Our mother had approached the local schoolmaster, to ask if Kathleen could attend the little village school once she was able to walk, but he refused to take her. My parents then felt unable to press the point, probably because most people at that time considered that Down's syndrome made the child ineducable. These pundits had, however, reckoned without the kind of personality our mother had - strong willed, determined, patient to the nth degree, and with a steadfast refusal to believe that there was anything her youngest daughter could not do. She was absolutely determined that Kathleen should have the best life she could get for her, the highest quality of life that she could attain, and she devoted her own life to that end. This involved patient repetition over many years for the two of them.

I went to a very small private school until I was ten, and then on very rare occasions Kathleen came there with me - the teacher made little attempt to help her, and she was not really made welcome. I think she only came with me when our mother had to go somewhere and was unable to take Kathleen. Nevertheless, the memory of those times stayed with Kathleen all her life, for she so longed to go to school, and she always referred to it as her "nursery-rhyme" school. When I went on to a convent school, they would have taken her too, but there was a two hour bus ride each way, and as the buses were unheated in the winter and Kathleen had circulatory problems, it was too far for her to go.

Knowing how much learning potential there proved to be in Kathleen - and her cry was always, "Show me, show me how, I want to know please," when she wanted to do something new - I do not believe she could have achieved more, even with the best teachers and schools there may have been in those days. No-one could have given her more time or loving patience in teaching than our mother, and she seemed instinctively to know how to get the best effort from Kathleen. Her often repeated advice to me was, "Never raise your voice, never lose your patience, and Kathleen will always do her best for you. If you raise your voice she will lose all her reasoning ability; speak to her gently, and she will do what you want." Remembering how eager Kathleen always was to learn any new skill, I think of the words of Robert Louis Stevenson: "To be what we are, and to become what we are capable of becoming, is the only end in life."[4]

Kathleen learned to sew and to do simple embroidery; to knit with such regular stitches one would have thought it done by machine. She never would wash-up, saying, "My hands are too little," but she always dried the dishes, putting everything back in the right place. She also dusted, putting every item back exactly where she found it. She loved colours and enjoyed painting and crayoning, but her greatest delight was in music in all its forms. She listened with obvious emotion to singers like Mario Lanza and Deanna Durbin; if she heard a marching band she would be up and marching - or if it was a dreamy waltz, moving gracefully in time with the beat. She had a wonderful sense of rhythm, and wanted so much to play the piano, but that never came about - I think perhaps we did not try hard enough to find proper help for her. From her very early days she enjoyed going to the cinema - Shirley Temple, Judy Garland, Julie Andrews, anything musical - and she longed to be up there among the stars. She went to the local musical society's shows, and sometimes had to be held back from joining the people on the stage, especially when she knew some of the cast.

As children, we had few toys - what else Kathleen might have achieved, given the wonderful array of stimulating aids there are today, one can only surmise. Yet we both found great happiness from our surroundings. We lived among beautiful scenery, and made full use of it - always on foot. We enjoyed all the scents and sounds of each season, in the lanes, on the farms, in the woods and on the seashore. Our village then was very small, and we wandered freely and safely, with everyone keeping an eye out for all the children. There were no restrictions on gathering wild flowers in those days; they were our treasures, and we knew all their secret places. Our picnics were carried by our mother in one small basket, with a sixpenny spirit stove and a tiny tin kettle to make the tea. In the woods we would watch the red squirrels feeding or hoarding the hazel nuts for the winter. We were always thrilled to find the first snowdrops, and to hear the first cuckoo of spring, and in the summer evenings when we went to bed we heard the haunting cry of the curlews as they flew from the shore to their nests on the fellside.

When winter came, our movements were curtailed, but we enjoyed our books, and there was music and laughter from the wireless. With sparkling frost or snow, and the black lace of the bare tree branches, it was still a beautiful world, despite the cold, which was so hard for Kathleen, and brought back my chilblains. We grew up closely in touch with the countryside - we saw and felt the changing seasons, and our lives were rounded by them.

Health and illnesses

A few months after her birth, Kathleen developed a very bad abscess in a gland in her neck, below her left ear, and this eventually had to be lanced. She was kept in hospital for two days - and it was then that a hospital official suggested to our mother that she might leave her with them, and try to forget she had been born. When she was six I developed scarlet fever and although she had put her arms around me to comfort me, and we slept in the same bed the day before it was confirmed, she did not develop the infection. I was taken away to an isolation hospital, and the house had to be fumigated - which was the standard practice for such an infection at the time. For some years she had the eye disorder strabismus - a lack of coordinated eye movement, but this appeared to right itself, before she was found to need spectacles for other reasons later in life.

Control over her protruding tongue was learned over the years. In the beginning, mother would put her forefinger on the tongue to help her to put it behind her lips. Then for years we constantly gently reminded her to keep it in - eventually we only needed to give her hand a gentle squeeze, and instantly it would be retracted without need for words. Finally it became second nature to her to keep it in all the time, unless she had a head cold or sore throat. However, when Kathleen was asleep her tongue protruded a long way, and needed attention every morning. In her early teens she was diagnosed as having a form of thyroid disease which was treated by thyroxine, taken daily throughout her life. At thirteen she had German measles at the same time as me; her eyes became extremely sore, and there was great fear that she would lose her sight, but all was well in the end. This was in 1940, when there was a major German measles epidemic, and over a thousand children died from it that year. There was, too, a country-wide drought in the summer, and our mother had to carry water to the house from a stand-pipe quite a way off, with we two children ill in bed.

In 1943, when Kathleen was sixteen, I returned to my WAAF Signals Unit after home leave and it was confirmed I had mumps. Although I must have been in a highly infectious state while at home, and had slept in the same bed, once again she did not take the infection.

At the age of thirty-six, Kathleen had what the doctor said was the worst case of chicken-pox he had ever seen. She was covered in sores from her scalp to the soles of her feet, even inside her eyelids - it was horrendous. Twice she almost died, but she came through. I had already had the disease when I was four and at that time Kathleen, as a small baby, had not caught it from me.

From the age of sixteen to thirty-eight, every month Kathleen experienced heavy menstruation, always with severe stomach cramps for the first few days. This left her pale and devoid of energy for the following week, so she really only had a fortnight in each month when she was her usual self - and this went on for twenty-two years. We would sometimes find her with tears rolling silently down her cheeks from the pain, and we would do our best to alleviate it for her. During these years too, she gradually had to have all her teeth extracted, culminating in a cyst forming in the lower gum, which had to be removed by an operation in hospital. I was allowed to stay with her, and she was only there for two days. She had never been able to eat whole food, due to her enlarged tongue, and this was a possible cause of the loss of her teeth at an early age. It was a tribute to her powers of endurance that she finally achieved well-fitting and pleasant-looking dentures, but it was only after several sets proved totally ill-fitting and unacceptable. Aware of the possibility of obesity associated with Down's syndrome, our mother took care to provide a balanced diet, with not too much sweetened food. Kathleen kept to those early principles, joking about having "to watch my figure" when refusing proffered sweets, and she remained neat and trim throughout her active life.

The War Years

In the spring of 1941, German bombers apparently mistook our coast line for that of an important munitions area further north, and our village and the surrounding area was heavily bombed. The Home Guard led us away from the buildings into the open fields for safety; the fells behind were a terrifying sight against the night sky - one huge sheet of flame from end to end, fired by incendiary bombs. The throbbing drone of the aircraft engines and the splintering crashes as the heavy bombs split the ground were very loud in our ears as we lay curled up together, pressing close to the earth in the field, hearts thumping, breathless and speechless with fright.

With no defences to repel them, for this was officially designated a 'safe' area, the raiders circled for what seemed a long time, dropping their load. It was hours before the all-clear sounded and we were allowed to return to our homes. Later the same morning when the full extent of the damage became known it was decided that we should go with our mother to stay with our grandparents. This was because as well as fire and bomb damaged buildings, one huge land mine had destroyed part of the main road; pipes had been breached and there were no service supplies, water, gas or electricity. The official view was that the bombers would return to the area to attack the originally intended target, once they discovered their mistake. The railway line had also been bombed, with sections of the track destroyed, but late in the afternoon a train was brought up to the south side of the bombed lines to take away those who wanted to leave. Although we were all in a state of shock, strangely mixed with a sense of elation at still being alive, with her usual determination our mother ensured that the three of us, bags packed, were on that train.

Among her cousins with whom she was always so happy, Kathleen gradually recovered from the shock of that awful experience. She had broken sleep caused by night fears for months afterwards, and for a long time she absolutely froze at the sound of aircraft overhead at night.

There was no television in those days, only newspapers and the wireless for information, yet Kathleen understood what war was, although not why we were fighting. She loved to hear Mr Churchill's voice, and often told us that she knew he would save us all. She thought that Hitler with his "dumdash" (his moustache), was a horrible little man, "with his Heil Hitler." She wept bitterly for one of her cousins who, aged only eighteen, went down with his torpedoed ship, and Kathleen always remembered him.

Kathleen aged 17 in 1944

Kathleen and her mother in 1948

'Now I can read'

Imitating the models seen on the newly
acquired television

Into Adulthood

Our early years were lived during the great economic depression which desolated the 1930s. Our father was well-known as an excellent gardener, and we lived in an area of large country estates, but big houses were closed and empty and the only work our father had for three years was helping to deliver the mail on Christmas morning. I remember, too, at the time of the Jarrow March, men walking south to look for work coming to our door for cups of tea to help them on their way. Although there was then privation in our life at home we spent long periods with our mother's family who enjoyed a very different life-style, so we had early experience of two very different worlds. Until Kathleen was twelve we lived in a small limestone cottage with no heating other than open fireplaces - very good in the summer time, but desperately cold in the winter. Our source of lighting was oil lamps, our only lavatory was outside and we bathed in a tin bath in front of the kitchen fire. We both had croup every winter, but whereas I grew out of mine, Kathleen continued to have chest infections and breathing difficulties every winter, and had many ear and eye infections. Moving to a house with central heating I am sure made a great difference to her health, and her life-span.

As time went by our cousins and I each found employment, married, went our separate ways, meeting less often, and Kathleen was left behind in a time-warp, remaining at home with our now severely depressed father and our ageing but indomitable mother. I do not know what passed through Kathleen's mind as she observed these changes in the lives of her close contemporaries, but outwardly she joked, "I'm one daughter-stay-at-home; I'm not getting married, and washing dirty socks!" - a remark that had a sound of our mother about it. Throughout her early development, whenever she queried her own inability to achieve, or participate in something, our mother would give her an encouraging smile and say, "Well, it's just your condition, my love," and I think Kathleen related her non-participation in the progressively adult life-styles of the rest of us to that response. She seemed to accept quite naturally, and totally without resentment, that some areas of ordinary life were denied to her, and when disparities arose would say with a smile, "It's my 'ondition," the explanation so astutely prepared for her by our mother.

A major change came in Kathleen's life when she was thirty-two - for then our father died, and she and our mother came to live with my husband and me, leaving the village they had known so well. It was a change for the better for Kathleen in many ways. She was enabled to have new experiences, and to see more of the world around her when we were able to have a motor car. She made us laugh when one day she announced, "I'm going to drive my own car, yes, a red one, and I'll pip my own horn." Sometimes not wanting an outing to end, she would say, "Go on Peggy, let's get lost," which I often had done in my early motoring days.

Television too now brought a new window on the world and although Kathleen was not an avid viewer, she had favourite programmes. She always hoped that by some magic she would appear as the central figure in This Is Your Life, with her name on the famous Red Book. The emotions portrayed appealed to her tactile nature and she wanted to share them. Once I found her looking hard at the back of the television set and, laughing at herself, she said that she knew there were not really any little people inside so it must be magic. When technical matters were beyond her understanding she called them 'magic'; having her photograph taken and seeing her image on paper was always magic to her, and when she had her own polaroid camera that was still her opinion.

After having made their home with us for eighteen years, our mother died and it took time for Kathleen to recover from the loss, for they had never been apart - but she felt secure in our love for her and she did recover. My marriage was dissolved four years afterwards and Kathleen, who had been close to my husband, came through that change as well, and eventually formed a very happy friendship with my new partner in life.

There were no special schools or day centres when Kathleen might most have benefited from them, but she still learned sufficiently well to find pleasure from most suitable books and magazines. She was able to follow the lives of royalty and the celebrities in whom she was interested. She wrote letters to friends and her sense of colour provided her with many happy hours making cards and pictures. Child-like occupations these, and yet, as with most women, she needed to know that she was looking smart, wearing bright and pretty clothes. Once, ready for a party, wearing a new dress that sparkled with tiny crystal beads, she looked down at herself then up to me, her face suffused with excitement, and said, with great feeling, "Don't I shine!" - and she truly did in so many ways. The trouble now for me is that, although this is still a beautiful world, when she left, all the shine in everything went with her.

Kathleen had quite definite likes and dislikes about many things when given the opportunity to express them in her own way. It would have been all too easy to persuade her to follow one's own ideas and yet, with encouragement, she was able to voice her own opinions and then was highly delighted with herself. The key to most attempts she made was encouragement, and lots of it, especially when she seemed uncertain or timid about something new to her. Given that, she often surprised herself, and everyone else. This tells only a small part of the complex personality of Kathleen - in varying circumstances a seven-year-old, a teenager, and then again perfectly adult, and all in the same day - but isn't that a little true of everyone? She knew so much more pain and discomfort than I have described: one wondered that her small frame could bear it so often and for so long, but she always bounced back with her happy nature restored to us and always she wanted to do things "like Peggy", to do as I did - to be ordinary.

Toolis[5] records the words of Sandra Jenson, a young American woman who had Down's syndrome, who was the subject of a successful campaign for recognition of her right to life-saving transplant surgery previously denied. Sandra said, "I know I'm retarded. I know that can't be fixed. But if I could change myself - I wish I could be reborn. I don't want to be slow anymore. I want to be fast. Sometimes I have dreams about it. I dream things like being able to tap-dance, or do a little ballet. But then I wake up. And I'm the same. I walk slow. I talk slow. My mind moves too slow. And sometimes that's harder than anyone understands. But I don't want to die." I know those were Kathleen's sentiments; she would, perhaps, not have had much to say about her life if asked, - she just got on with living it the best way she could - but she, too, longed to be a dancer. In earlier days she often said, "I want to be quick-sharp, like Peggy," and just as Sandra felt, when someone known to us died, she would sometimes say, "I don't want to die, not me, no!" Despite all her difficulties, and they were many, she loved life; she had a marvellous sense of humour, laughed at her own mistakes, was always kind and gentle, full of love, ever forgiving, and politely thanked all who offered her even the slightest help. She showed great determination to succeed in whatever she attempted. She was aware there was a difference, but she dismissed it: "my 'ondition," she would say with an impish smile.

I loved my sister very dearly; to me she has always been the bravest person I shall ever meet, and she deserved nothing but the best this life has to offer.

Appendix I

It was heart-breaking to see Kathleen lose all her hard-won capabilities during her last years. Our memory is the key to our personality - to our inner knowledge of self - and Alzheimer's Disease is the thief who steals that away, leaving a trail of devastation in its wake.

Having witnessed the havoc it wrought in my sister, I can find nothing of a positive nature to say on the subject of dementia. I hope that when any new and successful methods of diagnosis and/or treatment are discovered, people who have Down's syndrome, and people with other forms of learning disability, will have equal access to them.

Although a confirmed diagnosis of Alzheimer's Disease can only be made on post-mortem examination of brain tissue, magnetic resonance imaging (MRI) was first used in research in America in identifying age-related changes in the brains of people with Down's syndrome during their lifetime.

Perhaps, too, it will be found possible to adopt some method of special screening, and timetable for medical-surgical intervention across the life-span of people with Down's syndrome similar to the recommendations made by Lott and McCoy.[8] Also to provide early identification and treatment of medical conditions that are sometimes masked, due to an inability to communicate needs by people who have a learning disability, as described by Wright et al,[3] and thereby prevent suffering and prolonged and expensive treatments at a later date - and this particularly applies where there is no verbal communication.

For the future, should responsibility for care management devolve on those who are not health professionals, Wright et al[3] point out that it will be important that appropriate health advice is sought by them, in such cases.

Marler and Cunningham,[1] Wilcock,[9] Wisniewski et al[10] emphasise the need for full medical assessments at an early stage when the onset of dementia is suspected, since other illnesses that may be treatable can cause similar symptoms to those associated with Alzheimer's disease.

Wilcock[9] also states that dementia probably affects in the region of half to three-quarters of a million people in the UK, and that the size of the problem will escalate very rapidly, especially in the ensuing twenty years, and Greengross[11] predicts that by the year 2020 every second person in Europe, that is one hundred and thirty million people, will be aged over fifty years.

The Down's Syndrome Association estimates that there are thirty thousand people in Great Britain who have Down's syndrome, which is the most common form of learning disability, and that there are approximately six hundred live births each year, of whom forty per cent will have heart defects. Persons with Down's syndrome are known to be at particular risk from the onset of Alzheimer's disease, or dementia very much akin to it, at a much earlier age than is usual among the general population.[12][13] Other illnesses, such as epilepsy, may occur at the same stage as happened in my sister's case. As a result of their genetic condition, people with Down's syndrome often also have other special needs and risks,[14][15] some of which appertained to my sister, and in some highly dependent cases these cannot always be suitably catered for in private or voluntary sector homes, particularly if there is not a registered nurse trained in learning disabilities on duty twenty-four hours every day.

Largely due to modern medical technology, many people with learning disabilities now outlive their parents, and this particularly applies to those who have Down's syndrome. In any given Local

Authority Social Services area, there are likely to be about eighty people who have learning disabilities living with parents who are seventy-five years old, or older. In his study, Sanctuary showed that these people will soon have to be cared for by someone else.[16] At the present time while Local Authorities are finding it very difficult to allocate funds to create residential homes, Health Authorities are increasingly reluctant to admit people with learning disabilities to hospital unless they need medical treatment. Also, many hospitals where formerly people with learning disabilities were accommodated have been closed and, since many people who have Down's syndrome develop the symptoms of Alzheimer's disease at an earlier age than the general population,[1] difficulties arise because they do not then necessarily fit the services that are available. Further problems may also arise in accessing homes that are capable of accommodating those who have these dual disabilities, while beyond these considerations looms the question of vacancies. The problem facing our society is where are these increasingly numerous people with learning disabilities, and particularly those with additional age-related illnesses and disabilities, to live when they survive their parents, or when the parents become too old or ill to care for them? It was into this dilemma that my sister Kathleen and I were plunged in January 1990 when we were confronted by exactly this sorry state of affairs, at a time of great distress.

Kathleen in
1982

A birthday
party in
1984

Kathleen's
58th birthday
in 1985

Kathleen's 61st
birthday with sister
Peggy and the crinoline
lady cake made for her
each year by her friend
Percy

The Realm of Stillness

Alzheimer's disease has been described by Ignatieff [17] as the journey of a sufferer and their carer into a realm of stillness of the mind, from which only one will return. One traveller promises the other: I will be there at the end to see for the two of us; I will be there to tell what once you were like; your suffering will not be senseless; you will not be forgotten. But we should remember, too, that many have to make this journey without their own special carer. Alzheimer's disease first affects the part of the brain that deals with memory, and then moves to the areas which deal with speech, voluntary and purposeful movements, and reason. [18] Eventually, it attacks the parts which protect against infection. This was exactly the process that manifested in Kathleen, and I think it began in 1985 when she was fifty-eight years old.

We had grown up in a northern seaside village and in our later years, each May and September, I took a flat there for a fortnight. We visited the people we knew and saw again the places connected with our childhood. I felt this gave added continuity to Kathleen's life after our mother died.

On our way home, in September 1985, my car broke down. We called the AA who saw us safely on our way, better late than never. My partner Percy was waiting for us; Kathleen adored him and was very excited to see him again. I went into the kitchen to make some supper and quite soon he called, "Peggy, I think you should come here quickly." Kathleen was half lying across the sofa - she was absolutely drained of colour, but was conscious, because she said in a weak voice, "What's the matter with me Peggy?" I eased her on to the sofa. Percy said he could not find a pulse, and I phoned for help. An ambulance came quickly, and on the way to hospital she was given oxygen and I saw the hint of a smile in her eyes as she looked at the nurse. Once there she was quiet but a little less pale and, after a short wait, she was taken for tests. The doctor said these showed no evidence of a heart attack, which I had feared - and said it was possibly all due to exhaustion from the journey, the car break-down, and the rest of it. He advised that I should see her own doctor next morning and said that Kathleen would probably be back to normal in a couple of days.

Long after, I realised that this was when everything slowly began to go wrong and that it must have been a seizure or stroke of some kind. I had no experience of this - I had cared for our mother for seventeen years, for the last three of which she had rectal cancer. She had not had seizures and, at this stage, I never thought of one in connection with Kathleen.

From this time there were changes - she kept leaning far over to her left when sitting on her sofa, and I would say, "Sit up straight love, you'll hurt your back." Her crayoning began to stray over the outlines and her knitting would go wrong; these things had not happened before - but we both made light of it. She would ask, "Am I a 'chusance, Peggy?", reverting to her old word for 'nuisance', and we would have a laugh about it as we sorted out the knitting. At this time I never once connected these very small failings with anything that had gone before. The doctor we had at the time of Kathleen's 'collapse' had since, sadly, died, and there being no recurrence, the episode completely faded from my mind. After a while, I took Kathleen's crayoning books to show to the doctor who had come in his place. I mentioned the knitting and other small lapses and asked, could this be the onset of Alzheimer's disease? At the time, I knew virtually nothing about it - it was a condition connected with Down's syndrome and brought about a loss of former capabilities - that was all I knew. With these few signs I must have appeared over-anxious, but the doctor spoke very kindly of how we all lose some competence with age, and went to meet Kathleen, whom I had left with the nurse.

For about two years she had been having trouble with constipation, a change that was due to a weakening of muscles. She usually attended to herself perfectly well in the lavatory, but since this trouble began I needed to know when to give her a laxative, so I had to check bowel movements. We made a joke about my intrusions and she was not embarrassed. There came times now when she would suddenly become fearful on stairs or steps, and would become quite rigid. Then I would move in front, facing her, holding her hands, speaking gently, and she would relax and move forward. She was only four feet three inches in height, and was always very careful on stairs. During the next two years she had some form of nightmares - which also had never happened before. For many years I had an alarm from over her bed to mine, so that I could hear her breathing, or be aware if anything should go amiss in the night. She had always been very afraid of the dark and there was always a low light by her bed. There began to be bouts of loud sobbing in the night. I would go and lie beside her and gradually she would be calm again. Once she said that she had seen a man's face at the window, and once that she had seen Daddy in his coffin (he had been dead for twenty-six years, and she had never seen his coffin). These bouts did not come very often and phased out completely after about two years. One night I awoke and knew that she was not in her bed. I found her in the lavatory and she felt very cold - I thought she must have been there a long time, but we had a warm drink and she was soon asleep. The next day Percy put a buzzer alarm above the door; when the door was finally closed at night we switched this on, so that the next time the door was opened the loud buzzer would sound. But she never got up during the night again!

Another time, she was going to the shops with Percy, and I was at the door because she liked me to wave them off. She had her feet on the ground and was sitting sideways in the car, but by the way she looked at me I knew that she did not know what to do next. I ran out and spoke to her gently, easing her legs into the front of the car. She became alert again and was perfectly all right, but I felt such a cold fear. Percy told me that when I went out without her, Kathleen had started to ask him the same question several times. She would ask repeatedly, "What time is it?" (although she knew the time, and had her own watch), or "Where has Peggy gone?", things like that. I never found that she repeated herself in that way when she was with me.

I am glossing over these years - these are just some of the type of episodes. For most of the time she seemed as she had always been. No-one could ever believe Kathleen's age because she never seemed to change. She had the most perfect complexion and we put a tiny amount of make-up on each morning. She had lost a little front hair since her menopause some twenty years previously - so we fixed a small hairpiece in place, and I made soft velvet hair-bands with a bow to match her dresses.

During these later years she had her birthday parties at a local hotel, and we were fortunate in knowing some younger people who were good friends to Kathleen. There were two nurses and a young lady who helped us and one of them would take care of Kathleen if Percy and I were going to be out too late to take her with us. They loved her dearly; they were her very good friends, and livened up her parties for her.

In April 1988, Kathleen developed a very bad eye infection. It became serious, and resulted in her having a brain scan. She saw an eye specialist every year, and for some time, periodically, had to have ingrowing eyelashes removed, but when this infection developed he was away, so she saw a different specialist; after two courses of treatment it was no better. It was terribly painful, but she was always very brave. Then another specialist joined the first, and it was decided to send her for a brain scan, which had to be done twice, she was so distressed, and she was always cooperative when she knew people were trying to help her. There was no cause shown by the scan and after a third different treatment the infection began to subside. But there had been fears for her sight. Recent advances in the study of the chemical make-up of the body[13] have shown that in some individuals with Down's syndrome there is an increased likelihood that they will not have the antiseptic enzyme lizone in their tears, and this increases the predisposition of persons with this syndrome to eye infections.

Otherwise, life continued with its usual ups and downs and then in November 1989, when she was sixty-two, Kathleen seemed to become agitated and unlike herself. Melleril was prescribed, but I thought this seemed to make her more agitated, so she only had three doses and she seemed to shake off whatever was wrong. In the second week in December, I could see that she was unwell and called the doctor on the 19th. Our doctor's partner came; he said that Kathleen had a serious chest infection and I got the prescribed antibiotic the same day. I kept her in bed at first because usually antibiotics made her very sleepy and unsteady. She hated being kept in bed, but would soon settle down with jigsaws on trays, her books, and other things. The infection was contained but then I developed flu symptoms, just as Kathleen seemed to be on the mend and was sitting-up in her bedroom chair. It was decided to give her a second course of antibiotic (Baxan), because I had been sleeping in her bedroom during her illness. We had both had the flu vaccine in October, as we did every year since it was first introduced, but what I did not know then was that this time there was a serious epidemic due to a new strain of the virus. That winter about twenty-five thousand people in the United Kingdom died in the flu epidemic.

One day I asked her to come downstairs to look at her Christmas tree and her decorations, for she had always loved Christmas time, and had hardly seen them this year, through being ill. She came down with me, but then she scurried across the room looking like a little frightened rabbit; she had a hunted look in her eyes. She darted to the foot of the stairs and became absolutely hysterical. I quietened her after a while and persuaded her to climb the stairs, because I could not carry her. Suddenly she shot up like a rocket; she had never gone upstairs like that before. Nothing would persuade her even near the stairs again, and to get her to go to the bathroom I had to hang a sheet across the top so that she could not even see them.

Soon after this, late one night, I found her bed wet through. She got out of bed quite readily and walked to the lavatory while I changed the bed, but from that night she became doubly incontinent. She had always been fastidious about personal cleanliness - neither of us could understand what was happening, and I know Kathleen felt as lost and terrified as I did. When I tried to get her out of bed the next morning she went rigid - she could not move - and I tried so hard. I phoned her nurse friend to tell her and she said, "For God's sake Peggy, keep her on her feet or she could stay like that for years." I tried to get her up to use a commode but, with her legs over the edge of the bed, she lay on her back, absolutely immovable - and just then the doctor came. She helped me to get Kathleen in the bed, and later said that I was not to struggle any more - that perhaps Kathleen might not be able to walk. I can't begin to describe how I felt, but in my heart I knew it was so.

Arrangements were made for district nurses to come in, and Percy helped me to roll Kathleen sideways, in between their visits, to keep her clean and dry; but then, quite suddenly, his back gave way, and he could not help me any more - he was then seventy-four years of age. So I had to manage; I would get in front of Kathleen and lift her legs on to my shoulders and try to lift her bottom to get underneath to clean her. I could not roll her on my own to get the draw sheet away and then roll her back, she went so rigid, and I had not enough strength left. I tried to lift her back up on to her pillows by standing on the bed and putting my arms under hers, but my back would not take the strain. I was so angry with myself at my own weakness, because she was so small, but she became rigid if I tried to move her. It was even worse when the nurses came. At first, because she screamed so loudly when they moved her, I had to go into the house next door. I knew the nurses did not want me in the small bedroom, but I heard her, even next door, and I put my hands over my ears and wept until it was over. Melleril was prescribed and this time it did help to sedate her up to a point. I was devastated by the change in her - I showed the nurses photographs of her, crying as I did so, wanting them to know what a lovely, gentle personality she had, and that this was not the real Kathleen. It had all been so sudden - none of it seemed real.

I had slept in a bed-chair close to her bed throughout this illness, and one night I realised that she was sitting bolt upright - she must have bent over to reach her writing books and pen, and she was writing, or trying to. There were pages of part of "Kathleen" - she was trying to write her name. It was in all sizes, and she was trying so hard that she was making holes in the paper; then she threw the book away and the pen went flying after it. She was always so careful with everything before, she must have been feeling completely lost and frustrated. Another time, she looked quite fiercely at me and said, "I might die, you know." One morning, as I went to bathe her face, I found what at first I thought was a huge purple bruise all over the right side of her face and neck. Then I saw that it was tiny pin-head spots under the skin as if something had burst, but it gradually faded away.

Everyday seemed to bring some new fear - now she was not passing water properly since her stomach was very bloated - catheters had to be passed - but the screaming did not happen so often now. It was terrible to see her having to endure all this; she had always been so brave, and still was, but where had that happy, bubbly personality gone? She was normally always full of fun, ready for a joke or a song. If she heard music she had to be up moving in time with it, and her greatest ambition had been to sing and dance on the stage.

When the nurses came one morning - it was still only six weeks since all this began - I burst into tears in front of them. The doctor came later on, and she told me that I should let Kathleen go into hospital while I had a rest. Kathleen was very ill, and unless I let her go, I was going to be in one hospital and she would be in another. She had found a bed for Kathleen, and would go with me to see what I thought - I'm sure no other doctor would have taken so much trouble. So we went and the nurses there were very kind, although I was very upset. Later, the doctor came home with me, and said I should ring the following morning to tell her my decision. All that night I paced up and down, upstairs, downstairs, sick at heart.

After her mother died, Kathleen turned to me one day and asked, "What will happen to me, Peggy, if anything happens to you?" I could not believe my ears for a minute: I had not thought she would think so far ahead. It was a lesson I shall never forget. Later, I made arrangements to take her to visit a local authority residential home for people with learning disabilities, and when we left she said, "I could help them, couldn't I?" I had told her there were kind people there who would always be her friends, and would look after her if she needed them. The home was closed some years later, and a letter was published in a local newspaper, appealing to families to offer a home to the former residents, to save the cost of buying properties to re-house them - to my mind thereby reducing their status to that of any waif and stray. I had promised Kathleen that I would always look after her but now, just when she most needed me, was I to let her down?

Lines from a poem, "...the woods are lovely, dark and deep, but I have miles to go, and promises to keep, before I sleep...", kept running through my mind. I was sixty-eight and I knew that I was no longer physically capable of properly managing her care. If I let her go, I could help her to get used to being away, so that if I died before her, she would already be with others. It was the worst night of my life.

When morning came, I phoned to accept the bed for her.

The practice nurse came to sit and talk with Kathleen for the last hour, and gently told her what was happening - she was a friend, and knew Kathleen quite well, but we did not know if she was able to understand. I could not speak - my throat had closed up. The doctor came to see her into the ambulance; she was carried downstairs and I got in beside her. Then, as she lay there she lifted up her head, looked straight at the doctor and Percy, and in a firm, clear voice, she said, "Goodbye."

Into the Realm of Stillness

So Kathleen went into the Ferndale Hospital - it was the 31st January 1990, and everyone was very kind. They nursed her carefully, and she did not die, as had been thought most probable, but 'plateaued out', although the doctor warned that her condition would continue to deteriorate, as her illness was irreversible. The nurses kindly said that they needed my help to understand her, as they had never had a patient like Kathleen before. Except for an odd word, she never spoke again. They told me that a few times when there was a loud noise or sudden movement, she said "Good God!", which I had never heard her say. Later on she would try to sing the word "Always" from that song - so that it is still called Kathleen's song by a few of the staff who remember her. She used to sing "Old McDonald" with Percy very loudly, and she still tried to do the "E-I-O" part.

I would get her to do perhaps one short row of knitting. She seemed to like putting coloured circles on to matching shapes and still liked to hold pencils and crayons. I got very thick ones that were easier to hold, but she could only produce scribble unless I guided her hand. I think she liked my reading her favourite Rupert books to her. She sometimes seemed to follow a film on television and she would watch a favourite video like The Sound of Music without falling asleep. She enjoyed listening to music on her Walkman and often I just sat with my arm around her. At first she could hold a teaspoon to her mouth, but that did not last long.

During the first three weeks there, Kathleen was very ill, and no-one knew if she would survive. Her eyes looked very black - it was a look I had seen at other times over the years. I have since learned that people who have Down's syndrome are ultra-sensitive to a nervous system trigger chemical called tropicamide, which causes the pupils of the eyes to dilate, and the release of this chemical can be brought about by pain or fear.[19] It was this process which gave the black look to her eyes. She must have been frightened by all the recent changes in her life. I felt terribly sad, because I was sure she must feel that I had abandoned her to strangers, just when she needed me most. It is a sadness I still feel. She had gone, but she had not gone; it was a living loss. She never spoke, or smiled, or cried - she just endured. I believe she had forgotten how to cry, for during the next seven years she had a lot of pain at times, but there were never any tears, and because she did not cry, I could not. It was a sadness in both of us too deep for tears.

Kathleen had been catheterised before she left home, but soon it was decided that she was suffering too many urinary infections; the sister said she thought the catheter was more for their benefit than Kathleen's, and it was removed. I knew there was less strain in her face thereafter and her legs, which had been swollen, resumed their normal shape. We had to leave her dentures out because she could not tolerate them, although I got the dentist to visit to see if he could help but he said not. For all her life her food had always been pureed, because her tongue was too large to allow proper mastication, but the dentures helped to hold back the tongue, which she had controlled by will-power. Now the will-power and dentures were gone, leaving an altered appearance, and great discomfort from dryness of the tongue, unless it was constantly moistened, and she could no longer hold a drink to her mouth herself. None of her clothes were of any use, because larger sizes were necessary. She was unable to cooperate in dressing and undressing and her incontinence required a different style of clothing altogether.

After a while she was put in a wheelchair for part of the day, and eventually she had her own. I felt desolated when I saw it with her name on. The ward where she was nursed was chiefly used for rehabilitation and respite care, and for dying patients for whom no further medical intervention was possible - it was in a small community hospital, and there was no resident doctor. Kathleen was very vulnerable, her illness was classed as irreversible, and the doctor hoped that she would be allowed to remain there. However, after some months, there were rumblings about "this not being a long-stay hospital", and it was suggested that I should start looking for suitable alternative accommodation. Enquiries were made, and I was advised that there was no bed in our area, either in an NHS or Social Services establishment for the long-term nursing care of a patient with a learning disability, who had previously lived at home. The doctor expressed the hope that Kathleen could remain in the bed at the Ferndale Hospital until she died, and that thereafter it could be used by others in her condition, since the Health Authority had omitted to make specific provision for this category of patient, and because this problem would in future continue to recur. I was also advised by others to see my MP about the situation.

For some time I had been approaching voluntary nursing homes for people with learning disabilities across the county, and some local private nursing homes - twenty-four in all. Nowhere was there a bed in the voluntary sector; some had long waiting lists while others had stopped even keeping one. All declared themselves "packed to the doors" mainly due to the then ongoing rapid closures of hospitals for people with learning disabilities. The principals of some of these homes advised me that it would only be harmful to Kathleen to move her, since she had survived thus far, and she and the nurses had become used to each other, and the routine she now had. They also said that in all the present circumstances the hospital could keep her where she was - it was, after all, a 'community' hospital. In the private sector, some matrons of excellent nursing homes were honest enough to tell me that they did not feel they had sufficient staff to give Kathleen the care she would need. One, instructed not to accept her, explained to me that often, in the interests of economy, staff are kept to the minimum requirement. This meant that if there were several highly dependent patients, these economic considerations caused unacceptably heavy workloads, resulting in rapid staff turnover. This led to unfamiliarity with some of the needs of long-term highly dependent patients, who may have no form of communication, who then did not receive the quality of care their condition warranted. In one instance I asked if the decision not to take Kathleen had been made because the proprietors were apprehensive that others in similar condition might follow. The reply was, "This is a private establishment, we do not have to take any-one we do not wish to have here" - although there were some state-funded beds there at the time. That particular home has since closed. Another reason for refusal was "Seeing her might upset some of our elderly patients." When I remarked that no-one from there had been to 'assess' Kathleen, the reply was "Oh! we know - we have our methods."

There are some excellent nursing homes, and there are others of whom nurses who worked there said "Whatever you do, don't let Kathleen go there." In others it was obvious to me that some things were not as one should expect them to be. At the end of the day, these are all private businesses; they may be bought and sold, conditions then may change, they have to make a profit which can only come from their clients; and highly dependent patients are seen as loss-makers. That was the message I received from professionals engaged in the business during my search. As an official involved in the resettlement of individuals following the hospital closures very succintly put to me at the time: "The truth is, if you mention Down's syndrome, these places just don't want to know." The nearest Leonard Cheshire home explained that their organisation did not accept people over the age of sixty years, and that in any case, all their homes had long waiting lists - people were literally waiting for others to die. A Sue Ryder home, recently opened, felt that perhaps theirs was not quite the right place.

I had arranged to see the MP one Saturday, and that same week I learned that moves were afoot regarding the bed, and that an informal case conference with just the doctor, the ward manager and myself was proposed. The next day the ward manager, who had always been most friendly and helpful, spoke quite brusquely to me, saying that the home I had mentioned did not appear to be coming forward with a bed. It was taking too long, and something had to be done about it; so there was to be this meeting on Wednesday. I had in fact named a religious voluntary nursing home some thirty miles away where, if I was finally made to take Kathleen out of the hospital, I felt she would find some love and care, should I die before her. There was no vacancy at the nursing home at that time, and the hospital had said they would keep her until one arose. It seemed the ward manager had phoned this home and someone there had said there was not likely to be a bed for some considerable time - possibly a year or longer. At Ferndale Hospital local GPs had been allocated the use of five beds in the ward where Kathleen was, and the doctor said she was fairly sure that the others would agree to Kathleen occupying this one bed until she died, if she put her case to them.

The informal case conference, proposed for the three of us, proved to be made up of seven people, one of whom was a social worker armed with a list of local nursing homes. The upshot was that when I said I was seeing the MP in two days time, not specifically about Kathleen, but about the whole situation regarding there being no specific provision of long-term nursing care for those in her condition, everyone backed off, particularly when the doctor said she was not prepared to discharge Kathleen until a suitable alternative had been found. I came out of that room a different person from the one who went in. Some comments made by a senior staff member are noteworthy: "Anyway, the Down's syndrome is not active now," to which the doctor responded, "Down's syndrome, Sister, is a genetic condition. It does not go away to order"; and again, "Other people have to put their relatives in places they are not happy with"; and "The only alternative would be a psycho-geriatric ward." These remarks flew in the face of recent advice given by a psychiatrist who, at her doctor's request, had made an assessment of Kathleen's condition. He told me that some of his patients with learning disabilities, who had been discharged from their former places in a large hospital due for closure, had been put into nursing homes, and in some cases he was not at all happy with their care situation. He said that Kathleen looked very well cared for, and that it would be best to keep her where she was, where the nurses had become conversant with her needs, and to maintain my daily close contact, otherwise she would rapidly deteriorate.

During the case conference, with the insight I had gained during my enquiries, I felt unable to accept the social worker's belief that a suitable place could readily be found for Kathleen within the private sector, and referred to the opinions expressed by the psychiatrist. Though I felt intimidated and aware that I had no legal rights over my sister's welfare, I stood firm in my strongly held belief that anyone in her present condition, unable to move or speak, or summon assistance in any way, could only safely be nursed in an open ward, where she could be observed throughout the day and night. I felt supported in the knowledge that eminent professors who worked with people with learning and additional complex disabilities held the same opinion.[20] I was shocked by the manner in which the views of the doctor, who had always given the utmost support to Kathleen and me, were challenged during this meeting. Later, Kathleen also became subject to epilepsy and, to my mind, no sane person could possibly believe that she could be safely nursed in any other place than an open ward. It was well known too in those years, that the full facilities of this small community hospital, which had no resident doctor, were not being taken up. The following year during a public meeting concerning a ward closure elsewhere, when challenged by other relatives, a Health Authority executive denied that pressure was ever brought to bear at the Ferndale Hospital to remove patients to other accommodation.

Before meeting the MP, I had contacted the Down's Syndrome Association and Mencap, who assured me, as had her doctor, that Kathleen was in the vanguard of a growing number of people who would soon follow her pathway, and who would present a recurrent problem to health services. They advised me to hold to my belief that my sister, in her now highly dependent and deteriorating condition, could only appropriately be cared for in hospital, and that I would have their full support if any difficulties arose. A Mencap officer confirmed that no appropriate specific provision was being made for individuals in similar circumstances to my sister, and that, when families became no longer able to care for their relative at home, their loved ones were virtually "being hawked from door to door" for placement, and that this was happening throughout the country. He added that this concern would be one of the top priorities on the agenda at the next Mencap conference in 1991. Both associations also warned me that the NHS does not have to provide a hospital bed if it does not wish to do so, and can contract a patient out to alternative accommodation, although it does have a responsibility to take the views of relatives into account in making such decisions. Kathleen certainly was in the vanguard at that time (1991), and at times I felt that I was a lone voice crying in the wilderness.

When I met the MP the following Saturday, he agreed that the position regarding the lack of appropriately staffed long-term nursing care beds for people with learning disabilities and age-related illnesses was as I had put it to him. The Health Service had omitted to make specific provision for patients with these two fold disabilities. He said that he was well aware of the anxiety this occasioned their families, particularly so since his wife worked with people with learning disabilities, and that, perhaps, a type of hostel-cum-hospital within the community might be the best solution, but, as there was none locally, he would see what could be done to resolve our problem.

About a week later, I was advised by the hospital manager that the Ferndale had not been designed as a long-stay hospital and that as ward usages were to change, and as student nurses would be working in the wards, it would not be possible to have long-stay patients there. They could, however, offer facilities to Kathleen at Grange Hall Hospital. They would leave me to think it over, but in any case, they would keep Kathleen at the Ferndale until her doctor and I were happy about her future accommodation. Arrangements were made for me to visit the ward at Grange Hall, where the sister was very kind. They said they had not had a patient like Kathleen there before, but they would do their best for her and felt sure that I would help them to understand her. They were aware that I went to visit her twice every day. I was so upset and afraid for Kathleen at having to be taken away from the nurses who had grown used to her, that I was not in a fit state to decide anything straightaway.

Shortly after this, one morning in July, at 6 a.m., Kathleen had a grand-mal epileptic attack. She was unconscious for half an hour, and they said they had only just managed to save her - she had been very ill. She had never had an epileptic attack before. Almost three weeks later, again about 6 a.m., she had another grand-mal seizure and again she was unconscious for half an hour. At about the same time the very next morning she had yet another seizure of the same severity and duration. From then on, she could not even sit up; she had to be propped up with pillows on all sides, she was unable to hold anything, and she could not raise a hand to her face - she was profoundly disabled. Not long afterwards, when her doctor conferred with a consultant geriatrician on this further deterioration in her condition, the consultant took up her case and was able to direct her to a bed under his care at Grange Hall Hospital.

Kathleen had been at the Ferndale Hospital for nineteen months, and was now sixty-four years of age.

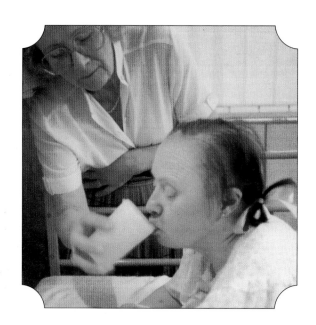

June 1991. Kathleen
was unable to hold a
cup for herself

Christmas
1992

Kathleen and Peggy,
December 1993

At Home in Hospital

After another flurry of correspondence between the MP and Health Authority Chief Executive, and a case conference at that level, on the 27th August 1991 Kathleen was transferred to Grange Hall Hospital where she was to live on for the next five-and-a-half years. Here the emphasis was that this was now her home, and I began to feel that she would be safe if I should die before her. All the staff at both hospitals gave her most devoted and loving care, and said they had gained much knowledge from nursing her. Throughout her life she had gracefully accepted her limitations, of which she was fully aware, and to the end there remained about her an indefinable aura that endeared her to everyone who knew her.

At first, I felt as though we were going back to the beginning; at times it had been difficult to diplomatically assist staff in acclimatising to some of the everyday needs occasioned by Down's syndrome that Kathleen had. I was apprehensive at having to repeat my role as Kathleen's advocate, but very soon there came to be a sense of being part of one big family. It is difficult for people who do not share their life with someone who has the syndrome to appreciate what is entailed; it is an experience which only other families who are in a similar situation can truly comprehend. For that reason, the Down's Syndrome Association is highly beneficial in bringing together these families, where they find among themselves true empathy and mutual support. There are very great variations in capabilities, achievements, and indeed in disabilities, among the individuals who have Down's syndrome, so that it would be very wrong to generalise, but it is a fact that many among them have happy, outgoing natures, and bring much joy to their family life, and that was certainly our experience. This sentiment is expressed in many publications, and in letters from families to the Down's Syndrome Association.[21] There also comes to these families a certain gravitas - an accentuated sense of responsibility - and the family knows an element of sadness that is always there, kept beneath the surface, while over all there is the fear, buried deep, of what will happen to this loved one, should they be left alone in the world. Such feelings are common, although they are usually kept well hidden, and bright, positive attitudes are outwardly maintained.

People with Down's syndrome have increased susceptibility to infections throughout their lives, some of which, in other people, would be common conditions of a minor and benign nature, whereas in these individuals there is a predisposition to more diverse and serious consequences than in the general population. For example, ear and/or respiratory tract infections in most people have very little effect, while in people with Down's syndrome the consequences may be serious because of the anatomical effects of the condition. The earlier the medical intervention in any infection, the more likely it is that the process will be satisfactorily resolved without such serious outcomes.[22][23] To the uninitiated, there may be occasions when the swift action taken at such times may seem to be a case of over-protection, whereas experience has proved that it is merely taking very necessary prompt preventative measures. Despite recent warnings as to the overall too frequent use of antibiotics for people who have Down's syndrome, their life-span would not have been raised to present levels without that intervention. Kathleen survived chest and other infections before antibiotics came into general use, but in later life she twice had pneumonia which would, most probably, have had fatal consequences without that medication. The most significant thing which can be done to protect people with Down's syndrome against infection is to provide optimal preventative medical care - the cornerstone of which is the provision of immunisation in its various forms, standard and otherwise.[22] People of all ages with Down's syndrome should have the routine provision of the pneumococcal vaccine, and also yearly influenza immunisation.

When she first went to Grange Hall I do not think it was the general rule for elderly long-stay patients to have the influenza immunisation, but I was insistent that Kathleen should have it as she always had done, and I believe that within two years it was administered to every patient in the ward. Although it may not prevent an infection, it is believed to reduce the severity of it, and that may have been why she was not one of those 25,000 fatalities in 1989/90.

At one stage, the level of sedation caused by treatment to control the epilepsy was such that some staff intimated that they felt it was unethical - particularly in the case of the use of Dantrium. After various treatments, including Largactil and Tegratol, and as the doctors and nurses became more used to Kathleen's reactions, it was found possible to control the epilepsy by quite low dosage of Valium, which was increased if signs were recognised that she was becoming more agitated; such signs could also indicate the onset of an infection, or of a bowel disorder.

In common with many who have Down's syndrome, Kathleen had a very enlarged tongue, and also breathed by the mouth, so the tongue became dry and coated during sleep. At home we had always gently cleansed Kathleen's tongue and mouth on first awakening, using previously boiled and cooled water, with cotton gauze. Glycerine sticks and other methods had caused allergic reactions. Unscented lip balms were in constant use by day and by night, otherwise deep cracks could appear - a source of infection of the mouth - and these balms needed to be in cream form, as lipstick types dragged the very thin skin. There was also a constant need for frequent moistening of the tongue and mouth since, due to the now pronounced loss of muscle tone, the tongue protruded and the mouth remained open. The nurses kept a constant supply of fresh drinks in beakers to use as they passed up and down the ward, for she could not hold them for herself. From the onset of this illness, Kathleen had rejected the previously much enjoyed and very frequent drinks of tea and coffee, but now even Milupa baby drinks and clear herbal fluids caused her to cough and choke. Then from the ward noticeboard I read a leaflet on aids in swallowing and drinking problems in stroke patients which seemed very akin to Kathleen's difficulties, so I asked if she could try the recommended oral thickening powder, 'Thick and Easy', available on prescription for addition to fluids. From then on this was added to all her drinks, and considerably eased her problem, except when the swallowing difficulty became exaggerated by the build-up of effluent from the otitis media.

Because of the sensitivity of her skin, a common occurrence in Down's syndrome, any soap would produce a facial rash, and this soon became understood. At home, only warm water had been used to cleanse her face, and this became the norm in hospital. The only mouth wipes for use after meals that did not cause a facial rash were cotton-based 'Contisoft'. Unscented Neutrogena bars for dry skin were used for her body. Due to the dryness of the skin, also associated with the syndrome, regular use of unscented creams was necessary to prevent scaling and resultant cracking. For the excessive dryness and scaling of the scalp, Johnson's Baby shampoo proved the least likely to exacerbate the problem, with occasional use of warm olive oil before washing the hair. If the scaling of the scalp was not controlled, it could lead to eye infections, and for many years the use of Hypromellose eye-drops, several times daily, had been prescribed to counteract the dryness of the eyes. Great care had to be taken, too, to prevent any water entering the ears, due to the presence of otitis media, a precaution stressed by the ENT consultant. Man-made fabrics had always caused rashes and excessive static, so Kathleen only wore natural fabrics. Both synthetic and natural sheepskins, now used to guard against pressure sores, proved too harsh, but natural lambskins, intended for babies' use, were found suitable. Underneath these, padded Spenco linings were used on her day-bed chair, with an orthopedic pillow to support her neck and head.

These needs may seem insignificant, but I stress them because they were time-consuming, and yet without this constant attention they would eventually lead to infection, distress, and suffering. They were regularly attended to at home, and they appertain to many who have Down's syndrome.

Due to the deterioration in her condition following the onset of epilepsy, Kathleen had become uncomfortable and unsafe in the wheelchair - more than once having slid to the floor, despite the use of a waist strap - and she was too small for the standard upholstered hospital chairs. Eventually the ward sister acquired a special type of recliner chair, deep enough to accommodate the necessary padding, in which her head and legs were properly supported; she looked comfortable and safe again, without the need for uncomfortable tight straps. Special castors were fitted, so that this virtual daybed could be easily moved from place to place as required.

It was of the greatest credit to her nursing care that only rarely did a break appear in her skin, and when that happened it was treated with the utmost concern - she was constantly moved from bed to day-bed, turned and treated, until it was healed. Every day, despite incontinence, infections and inability to help herself in any way, the nurses and other staff kept her person, her clothes, her bed-linen and her environment spotlessly clean, sweet-smelling and wholesome. Indeed, the same standard applied to every other patient; their dedicated and devoted service goes far beyond the call of mere duty. They even made time every day to put ribbons in her hair and that, allied to her small features and stature, caused some of the elderly ladies there to think of her as a child, and in their own way they would try to take care of her, calling the nurses attention when they thought she needed something, and asking about her if she was not in her usual place. I shall always remember one elderly man, himself dying from cancer, who said to me, "You think you're ill, until you see her. She makes you humble; poor little Kathleen."

To the End of the Journey

Despite the excellence of her nursing care, as her condition deteriorated, Kathleen endured many, often very painful, disorders, including throat and chest infections, and sometimes severe ear infections. Probably due to skeletal defects allied to the syndrome, it was not always possible for the doctor using basic equipment kept at the hospital to confirm an ear infection, although when very close to her there was an unmistakable malodour. When a swab was sent for testing, it could take several days for the result to return. In the interim, Kathleen would need frequent extra medication to offset the obvious signs of epileptic attack induced by the pain of the infection, and the rise in temperature incurred would be treated by antibiotics. Eventually, I requested an appointment be made for her with an ENT consultant. He had seen her many years before and on examining her now immediately affirmed that the condition was chronic and she needed major surgery on both ears and throat. He went on to say that no-one would contemplate operating in her present condition as that would be tantamount to euthanasia. At first he suggested that pain-killers would be the only alternative, but I pleaded for treatment, as the build-up of the very thick effluent caused her to choke even on drinks. He finally agreed to treat her at two-monthly intervals, albeit with some reluctance, saying, "If I do this, someone else is missing out." For the interim, he prescribed steroid ear-drops (Locorten/Nioform) for constant use, and at all future appointments she was treated with great kindness.

There were transient ischaemic attacks and grand-mal episodes, although the nurses soon came to recognise signs that an epileptic attack was imminent, and with extra medication this was very often averted. She suffered recurrent abdominal spasms, sometimes so severe that the pain restricted her breathing. A doctor would be called, oxygen administered, with sometimes rectal Valium or a hydrocortisone injection, to open up the restricted airways. Eventually this was treated with Merbentyl, and there were far fewer spasms. For some time there had been increasing need for enemas, and for the last year of her life these were found necessary about three times a week.

She contracted staphylococcus aureus, and had bacterial tracheitis, and for the last eight months of her life she had almost permanent oral candida albicans, and cheilosis. For her this was so agonising, with her enlarged tongue often so inflamed and swollen, despite treatment, that she could not bear the spoon feeding her to touch her mouth. Finally, when I pressed for an appointment with an oral consultant, the usual treatment by Nystatin was changed to Diflukan (Fluconizole), and after a seven-day course of that, for what proved to be the last eight weeks of her life, the mouth infection did not recur.

e doctors not to do anything expressly to prolong
.s clenched, shuddering from head to foot, her eyes
ng desire to put an end to it for her. I certainly lost
)ver us.

ied to have some respite, the nurses said that in the
ig about the ward, but when I got there to give her
:r her meal and the regulation dose of Valium. When
: would put her close by, and she watched and listened,
.ospitals entertainers came, I would help her to shake
over the notes of her small keyboard. She seemed to
;h coloured beads across a fairly large abacus and I
wondered ii i knitting gifts for her friends. After tea, if she stayed
awake, I would try to inteic i games, of the type small children use, holding her hand
to stack rings - anything with colour, sound and movement. However, it was probably her
music cassettes which brought the most sign of response. And then there were the dolls -
dolls that danced and dolls that sang. The speech therapist came once and felt she could not
help and the dolls were my attempts to encourage Kathleen to speak again. Some asked
questions and others said words wrong and waited for correction. It did not work, but I never
stopped trying, and I became well known at the Early Learning Centre. Her hands had
always been busy in the past, so I made padded towelling rings with a small soft toy sewn
on, and she held one in her hand most of the time. I knew it was a comfort to her, something
to hang on to - as a small child has a comforter. It helped to stop her hands clenching and
becoming sore.

We were encouraged to mark her birthday each year and, as he always had, Percy made
her crinoline lady cake. Kathleen had a pretty new dress, and there was music, with a
gathering of relatives, friends and the other patients in the day room. After her first birthday,
very few visitors came again. Everyone still loved her, perhaps even more, but the devastation
wrought in her by the illness made them weep - and not only the ladies. She had loved parties,
and "together" was her favourite word. I liked to think that she still recognised her birthday,
but in any case it was a need in me.

In 1993 I joined with others in forming the Lancashire branch of the Down's Syndrome
Association, and from its members, and from the Catholic Caring Services, we received
warm friendship and constant support. This led to a voluntary advocate who would continue to visit Kathleen if I should die before her.

Kathleen's wonderful spirit and the devoted care she received in hospital during her last
most difficult years were the main reason for her prolonged survival. I do, however, question
the humanity of such a life-style continuing for so long, although many would, I know, disagree
with me.

Many years before her decline began, Kathleen had fastened a label to the case where
she kept her writing materials. It was marked in large letters "PRIVATE. KEEP OUT." I was
delighted by her initiative and respected the message, although we laughed about it together.
After she died, I found some notebooks there; one or two had just one half-finished word at

the top of every page - the rest of the page was blank. These half-finished words were CROSSL... and HOSP... - Crosslands was a large convent nursing home, near our childhood home. This was where Kathleen had made her first holy communion. Our father was for many years their head gardener. Kathleen knew all the nuns, and we always visited them on our holidays. She knew it was a place where they helped people to get better. HOSP... was hospital - the other place where she knew people went. These pages were her cry for help. She knew something was wrong, because she was aware of the mistakes in her work and her knitting. She knew she could not finish writing her name and her words any more, that she needed help, and that these were the places to find it.

How could I not have known this was in her mind, when we were always so close, and I loved her so? People used to remark that I knew what she wanted before she spoke. I had not talked to her about the various lapses she had over the last years at home; I just comforted her at the time, and tried to forget it, hoping that she forgot them too. That must have been the wrong way to deal with it - she did not have the language to describe her feelings, and I had not recognised how frightened she must have been.

Crosslands was one of the nursing homes where I applied for a place for her, long after she had written the name in her notebook, but I did not know that at the time. Despite all their protestations of love for her, and all our family connections, they were never able to find a place for Kathleen. We were let down so badly by some church-based connections, I now subscribe to the theory that "religion has not lived up to God's expectations". Kathleen brought light and love and laughter into many people's lives; she deserved a better fate than this.

Due to a winter staff crisis at another local hospital, the ward where she was nursed was temporarily closed on the 20th December 1996. On the 15th January 1997 Kathleen developed a chest infection, and treatment by Cephadrin began. On the 20th she was moved with the other patients back to her original ward and staff. The next day she was thought not to be responding to the antibiotic and it was changed to Amoxycillin. Her condition continued to deteriorate, and by the 25th she was having great difficulty in swallowing even a teaspoon of fluid; her breathing became harsh and rasping. By the 1st February all medication had ceased as she could take nothing by mouth. All we could do was to keep her mouth moistened. The nurses were wonderfully tender in keeping her clean and cared for. I stayed beside her for the last four days and on the last day her harsh breathing became quiet and peaceful; then, at five-to-five in the evening, with just a little sigh, she came to the end of her journey.

It was the 6th February 1997, and Kathleen was in her seventieth year.

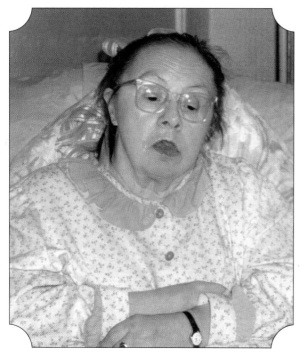

Winter 1994

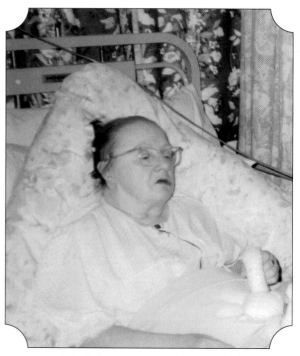

Kathleen age 69 in 1996

Thursday 6th February 1997

Appendix II

Dr Jolly, as Chairman of Faculty of Old Age, Royal College of Psychiatrists, said that, while most confused elderly people can quite adequately be cared for at home, there will always be some frail, vulnerable patients who are too dependent for nursing home care. These vulnerable patients will need long-term nursing care in appropriately sited and staffed small local community hospitals, with wards of up to twenty-four beds and Outreach facilities for day care. He said that when such patients become established there, with staff that have become well-known to them, it is essential that continuity of that care should be maintained. Otherwise, if moved elsewhere, they are likely to suffer transitional shock which often leads to deterioration and death.[24] This opinion is further upheld and explained in more detail in Thomasma et al.[25]

In my sister's case, due to a winter staff crisis at another local hospital, the ward where she was nursed was temporarily closed on the 20th December 1996. The eleven elderly patients were moved and separated into two adjoining wards, their known staff thereby being released for duties at the hospital in crisis. The temporarily closed ward was reopened on the 20th January 1997, and the patients moved again, back to their original ward and staff. However, over a period of five weeks, four of the eleven patients died, three of them, including my sister, having been there the longest - for periods of from five to eight years respectively. These figures would appear to give credence to the opinions expressed by Dr Jolly.

Postscript - Reflections

I was always so thankful for the support of the doctors and all the staff at the hospitals. They sometimes said that I knew Kathleen better than they did, but there was so much I did not understand about her in her altered state. At times, perhaps, I sensed a change in her before they did, for there had always been a kind of telepathy between us. If she was ill or in pain, she would develop a form of mental tension which transmitted to me, and that tension could lead to excessive twitching of limbs and an epileptic attack, unless signs were recognised early enough for extra medication to offset that. In earlier days, one sure sign of distress had been a drawing together, a seeming shrinkage of the tongue - it happened with any distress, dislike or fear, or even by becoming aware that someone was staring at her. It was as though the tongue withdrew from the situation, as she wished to do.

The nurses at both hospitals told me that they had never nursed a patient like Kathleen before. They had asked me to help them, and I was there every day, but even so, there were times when we all knew something else was wrong with her, but none of us knew what it was. The doctors eventually acknowledged that I knew something was amiss forty-eight hours before they did, but it still took time for tests to be done, and meantime Kathleen suffered.

There will, in the future, be increasing numbers of patients who have Down's syndrome and dementia. Some of these people will come to require long-term nursing care and not all will have someone on hand every day who has known them all their life. While no-one would wish to see any form of segregation, these disadvantaged people do have special needs. When they become older and ill and, most particularly, when they have no means of communication, wherever they may be nursed, be it in hospital, nursing home, or elsewhere, those special needs ought to be recognised and provided for by the presence of a nurse trained in the nursing of people with learning disabilities on duty twenty-four hours every day. Otherwise, there will be unrecognised suffering in some patients that could be identified, and given early treatment if a nurse trained to recognise their special needs was in attendance. At the very lowest level of provision, during illness, their progress should be monitored by a specialist nurse at frequent intervals. This is essential as these individuals are known to be subject to rapid changes in their condition, which may then very quickly become acute.

Professor Ben Sacks, Professor of Developmental Psychiatry at Charing Cross and Westminster Medical School, has said that he believes it to be utterly unrealistic to expect the private or voluntary sector to satisfactorily cope with people who have mental and multiple handicaps, and that those with such complexities need appropriate residential hospital care.[20] His opinion concurs with that of Dr Jolly, in that both affirm that there will always be some vulnerable patients who are too dependent for nursing home care, and who will need appropriate residential hospital care. From my years of visiting at two hospitals which catered for the needs of such patients, I entirely agree with their views. For confused elderly patients who cannot move of their own volition or verbally communicate, who can neither call for attention to themselves or press a button, and who cannot occupy themselves in any way, light, airy wards such as were to be found at Grange Park hospital, with experienced nurses passing up and down from one patient to another, observing all at the same time, are their safest and most companionable accommodation. The patients see and feel part of the daily activities of the ward, and have complete privacy when required. With faculties intact, this would probably not be one's choice, but when most or all of the faculties are gone, I maintain, as do the vast majority of families with experience of relatives at Grange Park as patients, that there is a need for long-term nursing care of the highest quality. It is, therefore, to be regretted that this community hospital, which so exactly meets the recommendations of Dr Jolly, is scheduled for closure, despite the proposed replacement by a different style of service.

The Alzheimer's Disease Society in 1993 said that where hospital wards have been closed, the government should take responsibility for providing alternative long-term care.[26] Some sufferers have been discharged from hospitals into private nursing homes, and there are now well over ten thousand people who need mental nursing care, who are in private nursing homes. From a recent survey carried out by this Society of fourteen hundred carers, one in ten of the carers reported that their relatives had been mistreated in residential or nursing homes.

The policy of central government, in closing many large hospitals where people with learning disabilities formerly lived, is to have only those who also require medical care living in hospital, with other people to live in various forms of accommodation within the community with support systems. This move to community living is very much to be welcomed, provided that it is adequately funded and that the definition of what constitutes medical care remains the prerogative of the medical profession.

For those people with learning disabilities who have always lived at home with their family in the community, the question of where they are to be cared for when their parents or carers can no longer continue is still not being addressed. There will continue to be sudden crises which may result in haphazard, inappropriate, and sometimes totally unsatisfactory placements, the resultant strains in some cases causing the break-up of families. In an edited selection from Hansard (1996), Baroness Cox (Con)[27] is reported as having raised in parliament concerns relating to unsatisfactory placements and conditions relevant to the care of people with learning disabilities.

In my own case, as a carer, three years after Kathleen went into hospital I was found to need an operation for cancer of the tongue. For a short time I was afraid that I might never be able to speak to Kathleen again, as already Kathleen could not speak to me. I was unable to visit her for three weeks and, although he had developed serious health problems himself, my partner went to her every day, and, for the days I was in hospital, he came to me in the evenings. At the end of three weeks the sister thought Kathleen was pining for me, and by then I was well enough to resume my daily visits. I was then seventy, and my partner seventy-eight years old; and until he became ill himself, Percy had gone every day to give Kathleen her food at lunch-time.

These had been very stressful years for us, and added stress now arose when the often published rumours of the closure of this hospital, previously dismissed by the MP as "paper talk", became fact. The Health Authority held public meetings to discuss this, and the proposed scheme for replacement services. A short time prior to this, new guidelines had been issued by the Department of Health raising the criteria for the provision of continuing health care within NHS hospitals.[28] I sought and received assurances from the NHS Trust executive as to my sister's welfare, in the light of these changing circumstances. The health service has acknowledged that people with learning disabilities are likely to have greater health needs than the general population, and may manifest at an earlier age health problems usually associated with old age.[29]

These guidelines also recommend that purchasing authorities should ensure that, where necessary, special provision is made where the health care needs of people with learning disabilities cannot be met through the ordinary range of services. The guidelines date from the 26th October 1992; sadly my sister's accommodation troubles arose in 1991, a year before they were issued.

Through ongoing advances in research and health care, the number of older people with learning disabilities will continue to rise, and the health service will need to make appropriate provision to address the special risks that affect these individuals. One example is the greater than average risk for people who have Down's syndrome of suffering the early onset of Alzheimer's disease or other forms of dementia, and also of developing epilepsy as they grow older. Sixty per cent of persons with the syndrome will develop epilepsy in the last six months of life[30]; and they also have other risks due to their genetic condition. It should be recognised that when nursing care becomes necessary, there will be available to them nurses who are qualified to nurse people with learning disabilities.

In a report commissioned by the Chief Nursing Officer in 1994[31] concerns were discussed as to the cost of nurse training for a specialist qualification solely for the benefit of people with learning disabilities, now that many are no longer living in hospitals. However, the need for specialist nurses did not disappear because their former charges went to live elsewhere. With the predicted continuing rise in the number of older people with learning disabilities, the need for specialist nurses should be considered ongoing, and not in decline merely because large institutions where they have been employed continue to close. Their specialist skills should follow their former charges out into the community, and could then encompass those who have always lived there. For some learning disability nurses, the only way they could continue in their chosen work has been to take up posts as care assistants in the homes where former hospital residents have been accommodated, although they are then unable to practice their specialist nursing skills, which become lost to those for whom they were intended. This loss is compounded by the fact that, in residential homes for these individuals, the greater presence of qualified staff increases the quality of care, without increasing costs.[3]

It is seven years since I first approached the MP about the lack of appropriate long-term nursing care beds for people in my sister's circumstances, which he agreed was the case, and so far as I am aware there has been no change in that situation. In the past, the area in which we live was known to look beyond its borders for care, when necessary, for those with learning disabilities. During the last three decades many large institutions where these individuals lived have been closed, bringing a welcome change in life-style for many, although not all have yet benefited from living in the community. These moves, however, have had no impact on the lives of those people with learning disabilities who have always lived at home with their family. No comprehensive register has been kept of their numbers, although attempts are being made in some areas to rectify this omission - without which it is difficult to see how future provision can be appropriately planned. Older people who have learning disabilities are often only discovered in an area when a family crisis occurs. Today there is greater awareness of this problem among service providers than appeared to be the case when my sister and I were faced with it. An ever-increasing number of documents and other publications are appearing concerning the requirement of services, including acknowledgement that, in some cases, there will be a need for long-term nursing care.

People with learning disabilities who have always lived in their own homes in the community have only recently experienced much longer life-spans than were previously predicted (this particularly applies to people with Down's syndrome) and are, in some cases, developing age-related illnesses. For these persons, it is incumbent upon our society to ensure that adequately funded and appropriately sited and staffed long-term nursing care is readily available when that becomes necessary. The difficulties and anxieties engendered by uncoordinated attempts to supply this need were illustrated by my own sister's experiences. There have been reports of harrowing consequences following the death of a sole carer, when a person with learning disabilities has only been found accommodation far from their home and known acquaintances. This, following closely upon bereavement, is a circumstance that should have no place in a caring community.

A very small percentage of people who have Down's syndrome may have clinical evidence of Alzheimer's disease between the ages of thirty and thirty-nine. Approximately ten per cent show signs of Alzheimer's disease between the ages of forty and forty-nine, but the figures go up to forty per cent in those aged fifty to fifty-nine.[32]

There is now repeated reference to the possibility of rationing of some services within the NHS. It will be vital to the proper care of people with learning disabilities that those responsible for health services keep their health needs constantly before the relevant authorities. This will ensure that appropriate provision is made, and that when these already disadvantaged people come to suffer further disablements and illnesses associated with ageing, they do not yet again become marginalised. In efforts to minimise some aspects, in order to counter the negative perceptions others sometimes have of Down's syndrome, it might be prudent to take care not to trivialise the special needs it incurs, to the extent that some necessary services might then be deemed inappropriate.

"Persons with Down's syndrome in some way reflect our own humanity back at us, and only our limitations cause us to fail to receive the gifts. There is a goodness, humanity, and magic in these persons that must be protected and never be betrayed" (Wolffe cited by Pueschel).[33]

These are the sentiments I have had in mind in writing this account in tribute to my sister, Kathleen, on her triumphant journey through life, despite all the odds, and remembering those who will follow in her footsteps.

NOTE

Pseudonyms have been used for hospitals, homes and some persons.

REFERENCES

1   Marler, R. and Cunningham, C. (1994) *Down's Syndrome and Alzheimer's Disease. A Guide for Carers.* Down's Syndrome Association, London.

2   Palmer, J. (1994) *Daily Mirror.* Mirror Woman, 16 March, 6-7.

3   Wright, K. Haycome, A. Leedham, I. (1994) *Evaluating Community Care. Services for People with Learning Difficulties.* Buckingham, Open University Press.

4   Stevenson, R. L. (1882) *Familiar Studies of Men and Books.*

5   Toolis, K. (1996) "A heart for Jo", *The Guardian Weekend,* 10 August, 23.

6   Esslak, J. P. et al, (1994) *Journal of Neurology,* Vol 44, 1039-45.

7   Holland, T. (1997) "Ageing and its consequences for people with Down's Syndrome". *Down's Syndrome Association Newsletter,* 85, 34-36.

8   Lott, I. T. McCoy, E. E. (1992) *Down's Syndrome Advances in Medical Care.* New York, Wiley-Liss.

9   Wilcock, G. (1990) *Living with Alzheimer's Disease.* London, Penguin, 5-6, 31-36, 89-90.

10 Wisniewski, K. E. Lewis, A. Wisniewski, H. M. (1992) "Ageing and Alzheimer's Disease in People with Down Syndrome". In Lott, I. T. and McCoy, E. E. (eds) *Down Syndrome Advances in Medical Care.* New York, Wiley-Liss, 167-183.

11 Greengross, S. (1998) "Agenda for change - Age of Reason", *The Guardian.*

12 Sawtell, M. (1992) *Your Questions Answered.* London, The Down's Syndrome Association, 5-6.

13 Cunningham, C. (1988) *Down's Syndrome: An Introduction for Parents.* London, Souvenir Press, 130-131.

14 Epstein, C. E. (1992) (Foreword) In *Down Syndrome Advances in Medical Care.* Lott, I. T. McCoy, E. E. New York, Wiley-Liss.

15 Lavis, D. (1994) One Step Ahead: Aspects of Sensory Impairment and the Ageing Process. *Focus* 13, 1-6.

16 Sanctuary, G. (1991) *After I'm Gone What Will Happen to my Handicapped Child?* London, Souvenir Press, 127-128.

17 Ignatieff, M. (1993) "A taste of ice-cream is all you know". *The Observer,* 5 July.

18 Wilson, K. (1994) "Diagnosis". *The Guardian.*

19 Scinto, L. et al, (1994) "Alzheimer's Test Breakthrough". Published in U.S. Journal *Science* 1994 - reported in *The Guardian* by Radford, T. Science Editor.

20 Sacks, B. (1993) "Mental Handicap Crisis as Ageing Carers Die". *The Observer,* 31 January.

21   Williams, P. (1995) "Should we Prevent Down's Syndrome?" *British Journal of Learning Disabilities*, 23, 2, 46-50.

22   Lang, D. J. (1992) "Susceptibility to Infectious Disease in Down Syndrome". In Lott, I. T. McCoy, E. E. (eds) *Down Syndrome Advances in Medical Care*. New York, Wiley-Liss.

23   Strome, M. Strome, S. (1992) "Recurrent Otitis and Sleep Obstruction in Down Syndrome". In Lott, I. T, McCoy, E. E. (eds) *Down Syndrome Advances in Medical Care*. New York, Wiley-Liss.

24   Jolly, D. J. (1992) Letters to the press, 27 January 1992, 9 August 1993, 14 April 1994.

25   Thomasma, M. Yeaworth, R. C. and McCabe, B. W. (1990) "Moving Day: Relocation and Anxiety in Institutionalized Elderly". *Journal of Gerontological Nursing*, 16, 7, 18-25.

26   The Alzheimer's Disease Society (1993) A statement reported in the press, 5 July.

27   On the Record (1996) (an edited selection from Hansard). *The Guardian*, 2 December.

28   Department of Health, HSG (95)8 LAC (95)5 February 1995. *Guidance on NHS Responsibilities for Meeting Continuing Health Care Needs.*

29   Department of Health: NHS Management Executive: Health Service Guidelines. *Health Services for people with learning disabilites (mental handicap)* HSG (92)42 and Annex A and Annex B. 26 October 1992.

30   Sourander, P. Sjorgen, H. (1970) *The Concept of Alzheimer's Disease and its Clinical Application*. CIBA Foundation Symposium Alzheimer's Disease and Related Conditions, 11-36.

31   University of York (1994) *Analysis of Responses to the Consensus Statement on the Future of the Specialist Nurse Practitioner in Learning Disabilities.*

32   Holland, T. (1997) "In reply to a parent member's question". *Down's Syndrome Association Newsletter*, 84, 35.

33   Pueschel, S. M. (1992) "The Person with Down Syndrome: Medical Concerns and Educational Strategies". In Lott, I. T. McCoy, E. E. (eds) *Down Syndrome Advances in Medical Care*. New York, Wiley-Liss.